An osbick bird flew down and sat
On Emblus Fingby's bowler hat.

It had not done so for a whim,
But meant to come and live with him.

On Fridays Emblus played the flute;
The bird now joined him on a lute.

The top of the zagava tree
Was frequently where they had tea.

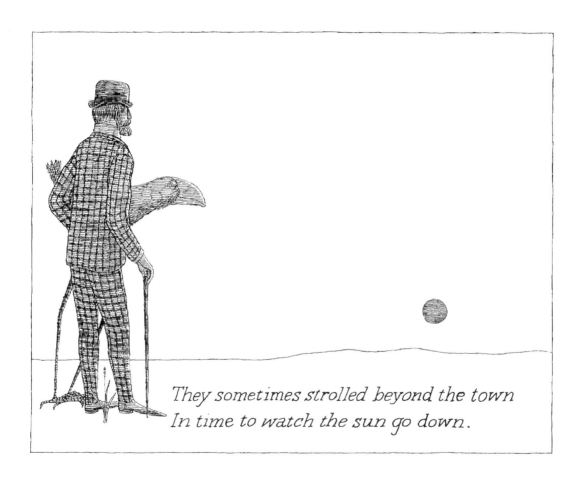

They sometimes strolled beyond the town
In time to watch the sun go down.

The cards got battered past repair
As they played double solitaire.

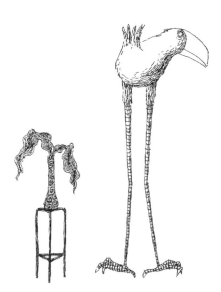

And after that they would not speak
To one another for a week.

They went to Periboo by car
And places twice again as far.

In winter they were both discreet
And wore galoshes on their feet.

Upon the river Oad the two
Were often seen in their canoe.

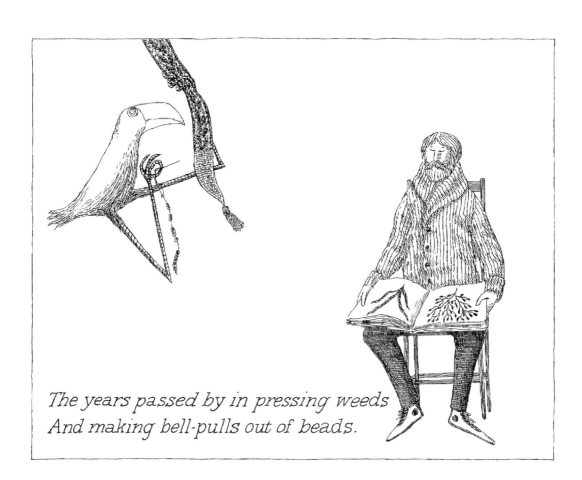

The years passed by in pressing weeds
And making bell-pulls out of beads.

And when at last poor Emblus died
The osbick bird was by his side.

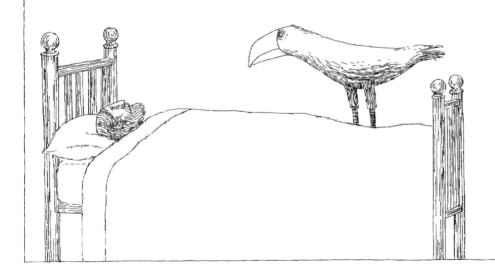

He was interred; the bird alone
Was left to sit upon his stone.

But after several months, one day
It changed its mind and flew away.

Published by Pomegranate Communications, Inc.
Box 808022, Petaluma, CA 94975
800 227 1428 · www.pomegranate.com

Pomegranate Europe Ltd.
Unit 1, Heathcote Business Centre, Hurlbutt Road
Warwick, Warwickshire CV34 6TD, UK
[+44] 0 1926 430111 · sales@pomeurope.co.uk

This edition first published by Pomegranate Communications, Inc., 2012.

Library of Congress Control Number: 2012935393
ISBN 978-0-7649-6335-3

Pomegranate Catalog No. A212

To learn about new releases and special offers from Pomegranate, please sign up for our e-mail newsletter at www.pomegranate.com. For all other queries, see "Contact Us" on our home page.

Printed in Korea

21 20 19 18 17 16 15 14 13 12   10 9 8 7 6 5 4 3 2 1